OUR PLANET

Rivers

RICHARD STEPHEN

Troll Associates

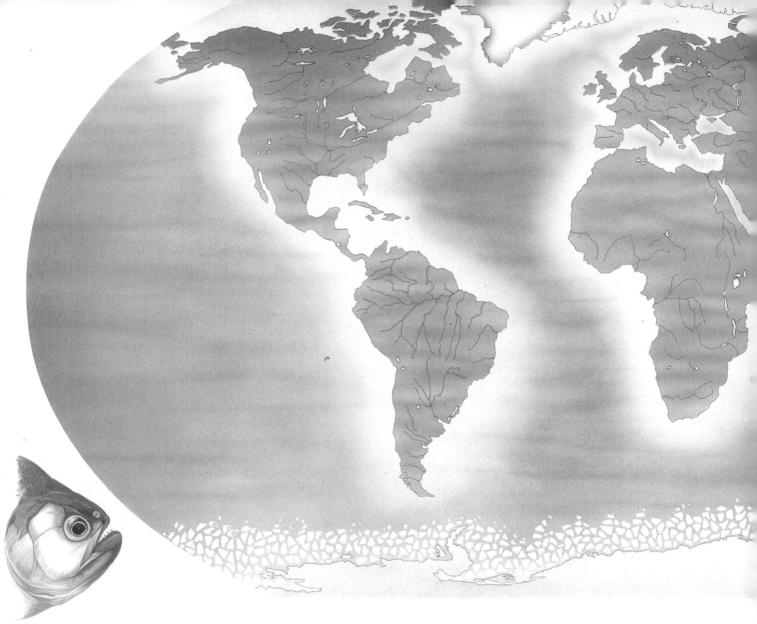

Published by Troll Associates, Mahwah, New Jersey 07430

Design by James Marks, London.

Picture research by Jan Croot.

Illustrators: Isabel Bowring: pages 22-23; Martin Camm: pages 22, 24; Chris Forsey: page 18; Mick Loates: pages 14-15, 16; Sebastian Quigley: pages 12-13, 28; Mike Roffe: pages 4-5, 6-7, 9, 11, 27; Ian Thompson: pages 2-3; Phil Weare: page 21.

Printed in the U.S.A.

10 9 8 7 6 5 4 3 2 1

Library of Congress Cataloging-in-Publication Data

Stephen, Richard.
   Rivers / by Richard Stephen; illustrated by Isabel Bowring . . . [et al.].
     p.   cm.—(Our planet)
   Summary: Describes the characteristics of the world's rivers, the changes that rivers make on the land, and the course of the river to the sea.
   ISBN 0-8167-1975-6 (lib. bdg.)   ISBN 0-8167-1976-4 (pbk.)
   1. Rivers—Juvenile literature. [1. Rivers.] I. Bowring, Isabel, ill. II. Title. III. Series.
GB1203.8.S84 1990
508.316 '93—dc20   89-20303

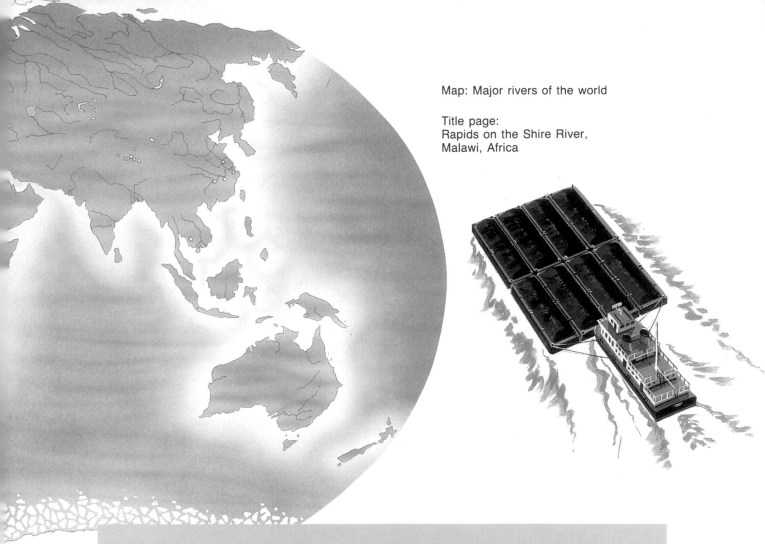

Map: Major rivers of the world

Title page:
Rapids on the Shire River,
Malawi, Africa

CONTENTS

The Life of a River

Water always flows downhill, finding the quickest route to the sea. To do so, it forms a river. Its *source*, the place where the river begins, may be a spring, a mountain stream, or even a melting glacier.

As it flows from the mountains to the sea, a river passes through three stages – young, mature, and old. These terms describe its course, not its age.

In its young stage, the course is steep and the river flows fast, perhaps over rapids and waterfalls. In its middle or mature stage, it winds gently along the bottom of a valley. Other rivers, called *tributaries*, join it, adding more water. In its old stage, the river's course is almost flat in places and it curves in large loops.

Glacier

Lake

Rapids

Estuary

Delta

4

Dam

Tributary

Tributary

The *mouth* of a river is where it joins the sea. If fresh and salt water mingle in the mouth, it is called an *estuary*. Other rivers fan out into a *delta* — a maze of islands and channels leading to the sea.

5

Carving Out the Land

Many of the world's most dramatic landscapes have been carved out by rivers over centuries.

In dry regions, soft rocks are quickly *eroded*, or worn away, by the river. But if there is not enough rain to wear down the valley walls, they become very steep. These valleys are called *canyons* or *gorges*.

Canyons are formed in the young stage of a river. As the water surges into cracks, it sweeps out loose materials and breaks up solid rock. The stone, sand, and *silt* (fine soil) swept along by the current carve out the river's channel. In this way, the valley is deepened and widened.

There is a limit to the amount of material the river can carry. As the slope flattens out, the water flows more slowly on the inside of bends and material is deposited there. But the faster-moving water on the outside of bends continues to erode the land, so the river begins to form a series of S-shaped loops. Eventually, the main current of water breaks through, creating a more direct route for the river to follow and leaving behind kidney-shaped *oxbow lakes*.

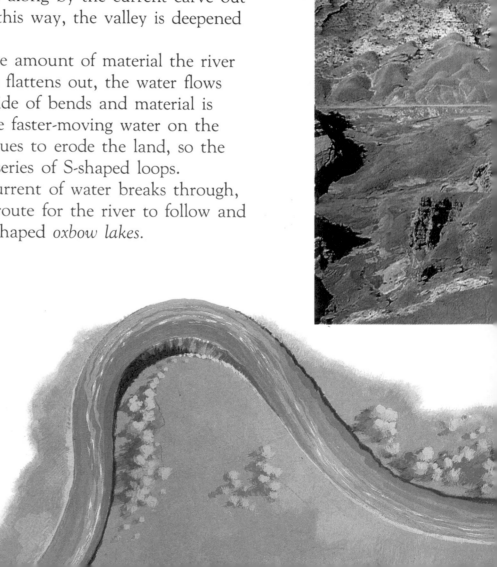

→ When a loop of a winding river becomes almost circular, the main flow cuts across the narrow neck of land and straightens out, leaving a *backwater*. Deposits of earth from the river gradually cut off the backwater, leaving an *oxbow lake*. The name comes from the U-shaped pieces of wood that were once used for harnessing oxen.

6

Backwater

↑ The Colorado River snakes through the Grand Canyon in Arizona. The river began to carve out the Grand Canyon about 6 million years ago.

Oxbow

Main flow

7

↑ *Valley glaciers* are slow-moving rivers of ice that form high up in the mountains. They begin to form when more snow falls in winter than melts in summer. Gradually, the snow turns into ice, which starts to move slowly downhill under the pressure of its own weight.

→ As a glacier flows down a mountain, it picks up rocks and other debris and piles them up in ridges called *moraines*. *Lateral moraines* are formed on each side of the glacier. *Medial moraines* are formed when two glaciers meet. Other land shapes are also formed, such as *eskers* and *drumlins*.

8

Valley glaciers are slow-moving rivers of ice found in mountainous regions. Continental glaciers are ice caps covering vast land areas. Glaciers are dragged by the pressure of their own weight toward the sea. Small ones move only a few inches a day, but some surging glaciers in Alaska reach a daily speed of 200 feet.

Glacial valleys are U-shaped. Many no longer contain glaciers but, typically, steep, high cliffs and waterfalls remain behind. A classic example is Yosemite Valley in California.

As glaciers advance, the debris they carry piles into *drumlins*, groups of oval-shaped hills, or into heaps called *moraines*. Streams flowing under a melted glacier deposit sand and gravel in narrow ridges called *eskers*.

Valley glaciers melt as they reach warmer levels. This forms lakes and rivers. In polar regions, glaciers extend to the sea, where huge chunks of ice break off as *icebergs* and cause danger to ships.

Medial moraine

Lateral moraine

Lateral moraine

9

Old Man River

The Mississippi River is affectionately known to the people who live on or near its banks as "Old Man River." Mississippi actually means "father of waters."

The river runs roughly 2,500 miles, north to south, down the middle of the United States. It begins in northern Minnesota and its mouth is in the Gulf of Mexico. It forms a natural boundary for 10 states. Along its course it is joined by over 250 tributaries, including the Missouri and Illinois rivers.

The Mississippi has played a great role in the history of the United States. In the days of the early explorers, it provided a route for the Spanish and French pioneers. Like most major rivers in the world, the Mississippi became an important route for transport and trade, particularly in the days of the great 19th-century steamboats. It still carries more than half the freight transported along America's inland waterways.

Cities and industries have grown up along its banks, and it has provided fertile land for farms and plantations.

Over the years, floods have brought death and destruction to many living near the Mississippi. In some places, manmade banks called *levees* have been built to prevent the river from flooding the land.

← Most of the freight on the Mississippi is carried on barges pushed by tugs. Paddle steamers **(opposite page)** are still operated for tourists.

11

Flooding the Land

When rivers are swollen by rain or snow, they often overflow onto the surrounding land. Sometimes the land can absorb the excess water; but if the rain is too heavy or the snow melts too fast, flooding occurs. In areas of low rainfall, the riverbed may be dry for most of the year, but violent rainstorms can suddenly create a raging torrent. To prevent flooding, riverbanks are often raised and strengthened with levees or dikes.

Floods are also caused by heavy sea tides. Barriers, such as the one built across the Thames River in London, are designed to stop the incoming tide from surging up the river and flooding the land upstream.

Nowadays we are better at predicting floods, but sometimes they happen so suddenly that whole villages and towns are swept away. In 1937, flooding in the Mississippi and Ohio valleys killed more than a hundred people and left a million homeless. When the Yellow River in China burst its banks in 1887, it flooded an area the size of Kansas and nearly a million people lost their lives.

Sometimes a dam is built across a river, deliberately flooding the land behind it and forming a reservoir or artificial lake.

→ Rivers rise after heavy rainfall and sometimes burst their banks, flooding the surrounding land. Flooding in the lower course of a river is often caused by heavy rain or melting snow in the upper course. Heavy sea tides may also cause flooding.

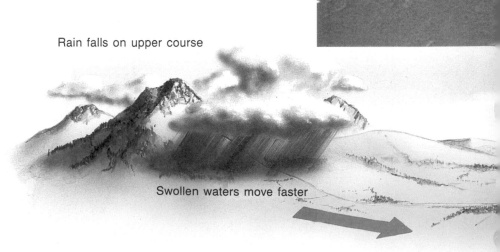

Rain falls on upper course

Swollen waters move faster

Flooding in the town of Nîmes,
in France.

Flooding in lower course

Heavy tide rushes upriver

↑ A modern dam is a truly remarkable feat of engineering. These massive structures, which may take several years to build, totally alter the shape of the landscape. As the flow of the river is blocked, a lake builds up behind the dam, flooding the surrounding area.

→ Beavers were building dams across streams long before people did. Using their strong front teeth, they cut down trees and make their dam with logs, branches, and rocks plastered together with mud. They often build their home (called a *lodge*) in the pond created by the dam.

Damming a River

A dam is a barrier that holds back water. It can control the flow of water or store and supply it to cities many miles away. The power of falling water from a dam may be used to produce electricity, or the water may be diverted through channels to provide irrigation for crops. The lake or reservoir behind the dam can be used for fishing, swimming, waterskiing, or sailing, and often provides a peaceful refuge for wildlife.

Unfortunately, if a dam bursts, it may cause more damage than it was designed to prevent.

Dams have been built all over the world for thousands of years. Early ones were built with rocks, earth, and wood. Today they are made mostly made of concrete, and may be as tall as a skyscraper.

In the animal world, beavers often build a dam across a stream to create a pond to live in.

Dam

Lodge

Underwater entrance

Waterfalls

When water drops suddenly from a higher to a lower level, it is called a *waterfall*. When the water falls more gradually, in a series of steps, these are called *rapids*.

Waterfalls can be spectacular – in some cases the water drops thousands of feet in a single vertical stream. Other waterfalls are wide, like Niagara Falls in Canada and the United States. About 84 million gallons of water flow over Niagara Falls every minute.

Usually, waterfalls are formed when a layer of rock in part of a river is harder than the rock downstream. The softer rock is worn away more quickly than the rock above it. A waterfall is created over thousands of years.

Narrow waterfalls with dramatic drops are formed in glacial valleys where the main valley has been cut deeper than those of the river's tributaries. The smaller, higher valleys are called *hanging valleys*. The rivers flowing from them have to fall thousands of feet to join the main river below. Waterfalls are often used as a natural source of power for making electricity.

← Salmon sometimes swim and leap up waterfalls up to 10 feet high when they travel upstream to their *spawning grounds* (the places where they lay their eggs). The life of the salmon is a remarkable story. They are born in freshwater streams, but spend much of their life in the ocean. Years later they return to the stream of their birth to breed.

↓ Little steamers take sightseers close to the base of Niagara Falls. When close to the falls, you cannot hear yourself speak over the roar of the water as it thunders into the gorge.

Spanning a River

The first bridges were not feats of engineering – they were just logs that had fallen across a stream. As the need to transport heavy loads across rivers grew, so did man's inventiveness in building bridges.

The earliest manmade bridges were *beam bridges*, consisting of logs tied by vines, sometimes supported by stones. The first great bridge builders were the Romans, who developed the art of constructing arches. The oldest metal bridge is at Ironbridge, in England. It was built in 1779.

Today there are many types of bridge, each designed to tackle different engineering problems.

Cities that have grown up on the banks of rivers often have several bridges connecting the two sides.

Beam bridge

Metal arch bridge

Stone arch bridge

Cantilever bridge

Truss bridge

Suspension bridge

← These six types of bridges are commonly built across rivers. Sometimes, part of a bridge can be raised or swung aside to let ships pass through.

→ A steel arch bridge spans the mouth of the Douro River at the city of Porto in Portugal. The lower roadway is supported by girders hanging from the arch. The girders supporting the upper roadway rest on top of it.

The World's Longest River

The world's longest river, the Nile, was the birthplace of the ancient Egyptian civilization. Today the pyramids, which house the tombs of the Pharaohs who ruled ancient Egypt, still stand near Cairo, Egypt's capital city, at the mouth of the river.

Over the centuries, the Nile's annual flooding created a narrow, fertile strip of land running through the desert. Most of Egypt's 50 million people live alongside the Nile today. To control the flooding, the Aswan High Dam was built in the 1960s. It produced Lake Nasser, one of the world's largest manmade lakes.

For years the source of the Nile was a mystery. The Nile has two "arms": the Blue Nile, which begins at Lake Tana in the Ethiopian highlands, and the White Nile, which flows from Lake Victoria in central Africa. Their *confluence*, or meeting point, is at Khartoum, the capital of Sudan. The Nile's furthest source – the start of the Luvironza River, which feeds Lake Victoria – is more than 4,000 miles from its delta on the Mediterranean Sea.

The Nile was once one of the world's great river highways. Control of rivers has always been important to opposing armies, and ruined forts can still be seen along the banks of the Nile.

↓ The Nile crocodile is found in most parts of Africa. This ferocious-looking beast was worshipped by the ancient Egyptians as a symbol of the water god who caused the Nile to flood, making the land near the river fertile.

← A felucca sailing on the Nile River. These graceful merchant vessels, with their triangular sails, have been a familiar sight on the Nile, and also on the Mediterranean Sea, for hundreds of years. They are used for transporting grain and other produce along the river.

21

The Mighty Amazon

In places, the Amazon is so wide that it is impossible to see from one bank to the other. It pours out a fifth of all the river water in the world, and for nearly 200 miles the Atlantic Ocean is stained brown by the mud the Amazon has carried into it.

From its source high in the snow-capped mountains of Peru, the Amazon runs eastward across Brazil, spanning nearly the entire width of South America. For almost half its length it flows slowly through the world's largest rain forest, a tropical jungle that straddles the equator and covers an area almost the size of Australia.

↑ The piranha uses its razor-sharp teeth to attack its prey. Amazon Indians use the jaws as scissors and the teeth as tips for poisoned darts and arrows.

The Amazon basin has been called one of the Earth's last frontiers. It is shrouded in mystery. Many of its plants and animals are found nowhere else. It is home to giant spiders, snakes 30 feet long, and sharp-toothed piranha fish. It also contains some of the world's richest mineral deposits.

The forest in this basin is so dense that most people live along the banks of the river. The Amazon has more than a thousand major tributaries. Even today, the river and its tributaries are the roads of the rain forest.

→ A water boa that lives in the Amazon and other South American rivers, the anaconda is the world's heaviest snake.

22

↑ Peruvian Indians live on the Amazon, where they catch plenty of fish. Away from the river, it is difficult to grow enough food to live on.

People and Rivers

Rivers have always been important to man. When the Nile flooded, the ancient Egyptians thought it was because the goddess Isis had shed a tear. A human sacrifice was offered to the river in the hope that the floods would subside. The Ganges River is the holy river of India. To the Hindus, it is the mother of all rivers. They believe it can wash away sins and cure illnesses. Each year, millions of pilgrims come to bathe in its waters. The ashes of Hindu dead are scattered on the river.

Almost half the Chinese population live in the Yangtze River basin. In China, thousands of people live on riverboats, and along the Yellow River houses are built into the hard mud of the banks.

The castles on the Rhine River in Germany were the homes of robber barons who made people pay to pass through the stretch of river they controlled. Many rivers serve as boundaries to nations.

Around the world, people make a living from the fish they catch in rivers. Large industries have grown up along the riverbanks, and many ports have grown into great cities.

Cormorants catch fish by diving underwater, then bring them up to the surface to eat. In Japan and China, fishermen train cormorants to catch fish for them. A ring slipped round the bird's neck keeps it from swallowing the fish.

→ **Opposite page:** Hindu pilgrims come from all over India to bathe in the sacred waters of the Ganges at Varanasi.

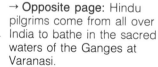

↑ Rafting is becoming a popular river sport. The rafters wear lifejackets and helmets in case the raft overturns when shooting rapids.

→ Boats pass through a system of locks to change water levels. A boat traveling upstream passes through a gate, which is then closed. The water level is raised to the level upstream. Then the boat passes through another gate, and continues on its journey.

Rivers are valuable for recreation. Many people in America take part in fishing, boating, sailing, swimming, and many other sporting activities.

One of the most exciting water sports is whitewater canoeing. The canoeists speed down a course of swirling water between rocks and over rapids and other obstacles. Rafting is also a popular leisure activity. Eight to ten people in a large unsinkable raft shoot the rapids of a fast-flowing river. But keep in mind that rivers are dangerous, so you need lessons from an expert before tackling some of these sports.

In order to make rivers navigable further inland, *locks* have been built through which boats pass to get from one water level to another. Locks are special enclosures with a gate at each end. As water is let in or out, the boat is raised or lowered so it can pass to the next section of water.

Before the building of roads and railways, rivers were the main means of transportation. Trading boats carried passengers and goods along river routes, and ports grew up to handle the ever-increasing traffic.

Water power from fast-flowing rivers was once widely used to run machinery. Before electricity was discovered, flour and textile mills and other factories were built alongside rivers to use this power. Later, hydroelectric plants were built where the water moved fast enough to drive turbines for making electricity.

↑ Machines called dredgers, often operated from a special dredging ship, remove silt from the bottom of rivers so they can be used for shipping.

Unfortunately, wherever people create and use energy, they also produce pollution. Industrial waste or chemicals from factories, radioactive materials, and sewage dumped in rivers can poison fish, plants, and animals. So can weedkillers and pesticides used in farming, if they drain into the water from the soil. These and other kinds of pollution sometimes harm human health, too. When a river is so badly polluted that plants and wildlife can no longer live there, we say it is "dead."

In many parts of the world, laws have been passed to stop pollution. But we are only now beginning to realize how important it is to safeguard our rivers so future generations can enjoy and use them.

→ Industry often springs up by rivers, as on the Rhine in Germany.

Fact File

Longest Rivers

The longest river in each continent is:

Africa: Nile 4,145 miles
S. America: Amazon 4,010 miles
Asia: Yangtze 3,915 miles
N. America: Mississippi-
  Missouri 3,860 miles
Europe: Volga 2,290 miles
Australasia: Murray 2,000 miles

Most Water

Out of all the water that rivers pour into the world's oceans, one fifth comes from the Amazon. It pours out 10 times as much as the Mississippi.

The Amazon pushes back the salt water of the Atlantic for over 100 miles and stains the ocean brown for nearly 200 miles offshore.

Widest River

The Amazon is so wide that there is an island at its mouth twice as big as Massachusetts. The Amazon is deep, too. Ocean-going ships can travel up the river for 2,000 miles, right through Brazil to the jungle port of Iquitos in Peru.

↓ Two-color river where the Amazon and Rio Negro meet.

Largest Delta

The triangular mouth of the Nile reminded ancient geographers of the Greek letter delta (Δ). As a result, a river mouth where silt has built up, forming a triangular maze of islands and channels, is known as a delta.

The world's largest delta is partly in India and partly in Bangladesh. It is formed by two rivers, the Ganges and the Brahmaputra, and covers an area the size of South Carolina. Other famous rivers with deltas include the Mississippi, the Yellow River and the Rhine.

Tidal Bores

A rapidly rising ocean flood tide can create a wave that rushes upstream from a river mouth. About 60 of the world's rivers have tidal bores.

The bore of China's Qiantang River can be 25 feet high and can travel at 15 miles per hour. The Amazon's bore is often 15 feet high and 10 miles wide at the river's mouth.

Highest Waterfall

The world's highest waterfalls are the Angel Falls, on the Churún River in Venezuela. From top to bottom, they are 3,212 feet high, 18 times higher than Niagara Falls.

A Spanish explorer, Ernesto Sanchez La Cruz, discovered the falls in 1910. But they are named after an American adventurer, Jimmy Angel, who spotted them from his plane in 1933 while looking for gold. Two years later, he survived a plane crash when trying to land nearby.

Widest Waterfall

The world's widest waterfalls are the Khône Falls, on the Mekong River, in Laos, Southeast Asia. Although only 50 to 70 feet high, they are nearly 7 miles wide.

Mixing Waters

When two rivers meet, their waters mix. If they are similar, they soon become a single river. Often, however, the two rivers are different in color and in the amount of silt or mud they are carrying. In this case, their waters may run side by side for several miles before mixing.

This happens where the muddy Missouri runs into the clear waters of the Mississippi, and in places where muddy tributaries such as the Rio Negro join the Amazon. But perhaps the most famous example of a two-color river is where the Blue Nile and the pale green White Nile meet.

Frozen Rivers

The biggest valley glaciers are in Alaska and the Himalayas. The Siachen Glacier, in the Himalayas, is 47 miles long.

But glaciers are not the only rivers of ice. Rivers can freeze over in winter, with ice thick enough to skate on. When a mountain waterfall freezes, a ghostlike curtain of frozen water hangs in midair.

↑ *Frozen mountain waterfall*

Index

Picture Credits
N.S. Barrett: page 19
GeoScience Features: B. Booth 6-7, 14-15
Remote Source: Emma van Gruisen 25
Rex Features: SIPA Press 12-13;
DPPI/Stéphane Compoint 26-27
South American Pictures: 30
Survival Anglia: Liz & Tony Bomford 1;
Dieter & Mary Plage 31 (bottom)
Zefa (UK) Ltd: 8-9, 10-11, 16-17, 20,
22-23, 28-29, 31 (top)